Weight Watchers™

MEALS IN
MINUTES

JO MIDDLEDITCH

SIMON & SCHUSTER
A VIACOM COMPANY

First published in Great Britain by Simon & Schuster, 1996
A Viacom Company

Copyright ©1996, Weight Watchers (UK) Ltd

Simon & Schuster Ltd
West Garden Place
Kendal Street
London W2 2AQ

Weight Watchers is the registered trademark of Weight Watchers
International, Inc and is used under its control by the publisher.

Design: Green Moore Lowenhoff
Typesetting: Stylize
Photography: Juliet Piddington
Styling: Marian Price
Food preparation: Carol Tennant

Weight Watchers Publications Manager: Juliet Hudson
Weight Watchers Publications Assistant: Celia Whiston

A CIP catalogue record is available from the British Library

ISBN 0-68481-663-6

Printed and bound in the United Kingdom by Print Wright Limited, Ipswich

Pictured on the front cover: Quick Chicken Curry (page 32)

Recipe notes:
Egg size is medium (size 3), unless otherwise stated.
Vegetables are medium-size, unless otherwise stated.
It is important to use proper measuring spoons, not cutlery,
for spoon measures.
1 tablespoon = 15 ml; 1 teaspoon = 5 ml.
Dried herbs can be substituted for fresh ones, but the flavour may not always
be as good. Halve the fresh herb quantity stated in the recipe.

Vegetarian recipes:
These symbols show which recipes are suitable for vegetarians.

Ⓥ shows the recipe is vegetarian

V shows the recipe has a vegetarian option

Contents

Introduction

If you have both a busy lifestyle and a passion for food, then *Meals In Minutes* is the perfect book for you. Packed to the brim with a feast of flavours and recipes which can be prepared in the blink of an eye, *Meals In Minutes* has been written with the busy cook in mind. Whether you are following the Weight Watchers 'Slim and Trim '96' Programme or simply have an interest in healthy eating, you will find these recipes tasty and satisfying – and remarkably quick to put together.

Being a Weight Watchers Member myself, I am familiar with the importance of being able to create a meal in as little time as possible – to avoid the temptation of nibbling! *Meals In Minutes* will provide you with a wealth of fresh, imaginative ideas that will keep you out of the kitchen when you have better things to do than slaving over a hot oven.

The quick-and-easy recipes are organised in chapters for Breakfasts, Light Meals, Main Meals and Puddings. Each recipe gives preparation and cooking times, as well as Weight Watchers Selections and Calories per serving, allowing you to keep track of your food intake with minimal fuss. So now you can create delicious meals at any time of day, without infringing on either your timetable or your waistline!

Breakfasts

Start the day as you mean to go on – these tasty breakfasts will give you all the vitality you need, and still leave you time for your coffee and morning newspaper! I've included a *very* quick banana, yogurt and muesli 'smoothie', a delicious sugar-free apricot spread which is superb with wholemeal toast, muffins or crumpets, and some tempting hot dishes too.

Banana and Muesli Smoothie

This breakfast is very quick to prepare and will give you instant energy. I have used bio yogurt as it has a milder flavour, but you can use low-fat natural yogurt if you prefer.

Serves: 1
Preparation and cooking time: 2 minutes
Freezing: not recommended
Selections per serving: $^1/_2$ Carbohydrate; 1$^1/_2$ Fruit; 1 Milk
Calories per serving: 225

Ⓥ

1 small ripe banana, chopped roughly
5 fl oz (150 ml) low-fat natural bio yogurt
$^1/_4$ oz (7 g) bran flakes or wheat flakes
$^1/_4$ oz (7 g) oats
$^1/_2$ oz (15 g) mixed dried fruit (e.g. raisins, sultanas, chopped apricots and dates)

❶ Mash the banana well and stir it thoroughly into the yogurt, or whizz them together in a food processor. Spoon into a serving dish.

❷ Mix together the remaining ingredients and sprinkle over the top. Serve at once.

Variations: for an even speedier version, simply sprinkle 1 oz (30 g) sugar-free muesli over the yogurt and banana mixture. This would increase the Carbohydrate Selection to 1 and the Fruit Selection would also become 1.

Banana and Muesli Smoothie

Banana Bagels

Bagels have a delicious rich flavour and a slightly chewy texture which makes them really satisfying. Keep an eye out for fresh bagels in your supermarket, in-store bakery or local bakery as they are much better than the packaged varieties.

Serves: 2
Preparation and cooking time: 2 minutes
Freezing: not recommended
Selections per serving: 1 Carbohydrate; ¹/₂ Fat; 1 Fruit; ¹/₂ Protein; 10 Optional Calories
Calories per serving: 235

2 oz (60 g) bagel, halved
2 oz (60 g) low-fat soft cheese
1 teaspoon honey
2 teaspoons low-fat spread
2 small bananas, sliced

Ⓥ

❶ Place the bagel halves, cut side up, in a hot oven, for 1–2 minutes, or until crisp.
❷ Meanwhile, beat the cheese with the honey until smooth.
❸ Spread each bagel half with 1 teaspoon of low-fat spread and half of the cream cheese mixture. Top with the sliced banana and eat warm.

Cook's note: you can use a muffin instead of a bagel – the spiced fruit ones are particularly tasty!

Fruity French Toast

These cinnamon-flavoured french toasts make a warm and filling breakfast – a great way to start those mornings when you wake up with a real hunger!

Serves: 2
Preparation and cooking time: 5 minutes
Freezing: not recommended
Selections per serving: 1 Carbohydrate; ¹/₂ Fat; ¹/₂ Protein; 10 Optional Calories
Calories per serving: 175

1 egg
1 tablespoon milk
2 × 1 oz (30 g) slices of fruited bread
1 teaspoon vegetable oil
¹/₂ teaspoon caster sugar
a generous pinch of ground cinnamon

Ⓥ if using a free-range egg

❶ Beat the egg and milk together in a shallow dish. Place the slices of fruit bread in the dish to soak up the egg liquid.
❷ Lightly grease a non-stick, heavy-based frying pan with the oil, and heat to a medium temperature. Add the bread and cook for about ¹/₂ minute on each side, until golden.
❸ Mix together the sugar and cinnamon and sprinkle over the toasts. Serve hot.

Variation: ordinary sliced white or brown bread can be used in place of the fruited bread.

Lemon and Sultana Pancakes

These pancakes are an ideal breakfast treat at the weekend, and can be enjoyed by the whole family.
They are also delicious served as a dessert.

Serves: 4 (makes 8)
Preparation and cooking time: 12 minutes
Freezing: not recommended
Selections per serving: 1 Carbohydrate; 1 Fruit;
  ^{1}/$_2$ Protein; 70 Optional Calories
Calories per serving: 235

Ⓥ if using a free-range egg

4 oz (120 g) self-raising flour
a pinch of salt
2 tablespoons caster sugar
1 egg, beaten
^{1}/$_4$ **pint (150 ml) semi-skimmed milk**
grated zest of 1 lemon
2 oz (60 g) sultanas
1 teaspoon sunflower oil
To serve:
8 oz (240 g) raspberries
4 oz (120 g) low-fat fromage frais

❶ Sieve the flour, salt and sugar into a large bowl.
❷ Make a well in the centre, add the beaten egg and half of the milk and beat well. Gradually beat in the remaining milk to make a thick batter. Fold in the lemon zest and sultanas.
❸ Lightly oil a large, heavy-based frying pan or griddle and heat to medium temperature. Drop 4 spoonfuls of the batter into the pan, well spaced apart.
❹ Cook for 1–2 minutes, or until bubbles form on the surface of the pancakes. Flip the pancakes over,

using a palette knife, and cook for 1–2 minutes more, until golden. Cover and keep warm while you cook the remaining pancakes.
❺ Serve the pancakes warm, with the raspberries and fromage frais.

Cook's note: serve the pancakes simply with 1 tablespoon of maple syrup or honey. This will alter the Selections to 1 Carbohydrate; ^{1}/$_2$ Fruit; 85 Optional Calories.

Mushroom Soufflé Omelette

The egg white is whisked separately before being folded in with the omelette mixture, to give a wonderful fluffy texture.

Serves: 1
Preparation and cooking time: 12 minutes
Freezing: not recommended
Selections per serving: 1 Fat; 1 Protein;
   1 Vegetable; 40 Optional Calories
Calories per serving: 175

V if using a free-range egg and vegetarian parmesan

$^1/_2$ **teaspoon sunflower oil**
4 oz (120 g) mushrooms, sliced
1 egg, separated
2 tablespoons skimmed milk
$^1/_2$ **teaspoon sunflower margarine**
1 tablespoon freshly grated parmesan cheese
salt and freshly ground black pepper

❶ Heat the oil in a small pan and sauté the mushrooms for 2–3 minutes, until tender. Remove from the pan.
❷ Beat the egg yolk with the milk and seasoning. Whisk the egg white in a clean bowl until light and fluffy. Fold it into the egg yolk, using a metal spoon.
❸ Melt the margarine in a small, heavy-based non-stick frying pan and pour in the egg mixture. Cook over a moderate heat for 1–2 minutes, or until the underside is golden. Preheat the grill.
❹ Scatter the cooked mushrooms over the omelette, and sprinkle on the cheese. Flip one edge over and place under the grill for 2–3 minutes, until golden. Serve at once.

Apricot Spread

This apricot spread is a delicious and healthy alternative to jam. Dried apricots are naturally sweet, so the spread needs no added sugar. It's handy too, as it will keep for up to 4 weeks in the refrigerator.

Makes: 12 × 2-teaspoon servings
Preparation and cooking time: 22 minutes
Freezing: not recommended
Selections per serving: 1/2 Fruit; 20 Optional
  Calories
Calories per serving: 50

(V)

8 oz (240 g) ready-to-eat dried apricots,
  chopped roughly
8 fl oz (240 ml) unsweetened orange juice
grated zest of 1/2 lemon
a pinch of ground cinnamon

❶ Place all of the ingredients in a saucepan and bring to the boil. Reduce the heat and simmer gently for 20 minutes, until the apricots are soft.
❷ Purée the mixture in a blender or food processor until smooth.
❸ Transfer to a jar or plastic container, to allow to cool, and then refrigerate.

Cook's note: if you serve the apricot spread on a 1 oz (30 g) slice of wholemeal toast with 1 teaspoon low-fat spread, the Selections will be 1 Carbohydrate; 1/2 Fat; 1/2 Fruit; 20 Optional Calories.

Variation: top 5 fl oz (150 ml) of low-fat natural yogurt with 4 teaspoons of the apricot spread. This will use 1 Fruit Selection, 1 Milk Selection and 40 Optional Calories.

Light Meals

Light Meals are ideal for lunch or supper, or can be cleverly combined with a pudding and eaten as a Main Meal.

Inspirational recipes include a rustic garlicky Mediterranean-style soup, an Asian stir-fry with an amazing peanut sauce, and a collection of savoury filled baguettes.

Prawn and Cheese Toasties

Any hard cheese can be used for these speedy toasts, making them a great way to use up odd bits and pieces lurking in the fridge!

Serves: 1
Preparation and cooking time: 5 minutes
Freezing: not recommended
Selections per serving: 2 Carbohydrate; 1 Fat; 2 Protein; 1/4 Vegetable
Calories per serving: 365

1 teaspoon olive oil
2 oz (60 g) slice of country-style French
   or Italian bread
1 garlic clove, halved
1 tablespoon finely chopped red onion
1 mushroom, sliced
2 oz (60 g) cooked peeled prawns
1 oz (30 g) cheese, grated or crumbled
   (e.g. Cheddar, Stilton, red Leicester,
   Wensleydale, or feta)

1 Drizzle the oil over the bread and toast both sides lightly under a preheated grill.
2 Rub the toasted bread with the cut edges of the garlic and then discard the clove. Top the bread with the onion, mushroom and prawns. Sprinkle with cheese.

3 Return the toast to under the grill and cook until the cheese has melted and turned golden.

Cook's note: plain sliced bread works just as well.

Prawn and Cheese Toasties

Pork and Noodle Stir-fry

I find egg noodles really satisfying – especially with this rich and spicy peanut sauce. This recipe is a particular favourite as I used to avoid peanut sauces, since they are usually laden with Calories!

Serves: 2
Preparation and cooking time: 15 minutes
Freezing: not recommended
Selections per serving: 1 Carbohydrate; 1 Fat; 2 Protein; 2 Vegetable; 155 Optional Calories
Calories per serving: 465

V

2 oz (60 g) egg noodles
2 teaspoons sunflower oil
4 oz (120 g) lean pork, diced
1 garlic clove, crushed
1 small leek, shredded
1 carrot, cut in strips
$^1/_2$ red pepper, cored, de-seeded and cut in strips

$^1/_2$ **yellow pepper, cored, de-seeded and cut in strips**
2 oz (60 g) mange tout or sugarsnap peas
3 oz (90 g) baby sweetcorn, halved lengthways
3 oz (90 g) beansprouts
2 Chinese leaves, shredded
1–2 tablespoons soy sauce

For the sauce:
$^1/_2$ teaspoon sunflower oil
1 garlic clove, crushed
1 teaspoon grated fresh root ginger
2 tablespoons crunchy peanut butter
6 tablespoons boiling water
$^1/_4$–$^1/_2$ teaspoon chilli sauce
$^1/_2$ oz (15 g) salted peanuts, chopped, to garnish

❶ Cook the noodles in a large pan of boiling water for 3 minutes until soft. Drain well.
❷ To make the sauce, heat the oil in a small pan and gently cook the garlic and ginger for 1 minute. Meanwhile, mix the peanut butter with the boiling water, and then add to the pan with the chilli sauce. Stir over a medium heat until well combined, and keep warm.
❸ Heat the oil for the stir-fry in a wok or frying pan, and stir-fry the pork until browned all over.
❹ Add the garlic, leek, carrot, and peppers and stir-fry for 3 minutes. Stir in the peas, baby sweetcorn and beansprouts and cook for 2 minutes more.
❺ Add the Chinese leaves and drained noodles and heat through. Sprinkle with the soy sauce and pile on serving plates.
❻ Drizzle the peanut sauce over the stir-fry, sprinkle with the chopped nuts and serve at once.

V **Vegetarian option:** replace the pork with 4 oz (120 g) of marinated tofu and reduce the Protein Selection to 1 per serving.

Speedy Savoury Tarts

These tasty tarts are similar in concept to a pizza, but have a light and flaky puff pastry base. I have included a choice of two toppings for variety.

Serves: 1
Preparation and cooking time: 20 minutes
Freezing: not recommended
Selections per serving: see individual toppings
Calories per serving: see individual toppings

1¹/₂ oz (45 g) puff pastry
1 teaspoon plain white flour
For the Tomato and Four-Cheese Topping
(400 Calories/2 Protein; 1 Vegetable;
195 Optional Calories):
1 teaspoon pesto sauce
1 tomato, sliced
1 slice of red onion

1 oz (30 g) mozzarella cheese, chopped
¹/₂ oz (15 g) feta or Wensleydale cheese,
crumbled
1 oz (30 g) low-fat soft garlic and herb flavoured
cheese
¹/₂ teaspoon freshly grated parmesan cheese
For the Ham, Mushroom and Cheese Topping
(345 Calories/2 Protein; 1 Vegetable;
180 Optional Calories):
1 teaspoon tomato purée
1 oz (30 g) smoked ham, chopped
2 button mushrooms, sliced
1 slice of onion
1 oz (30 g) Cheddar cheese, grated

❶ Preheat the oven to Gas Mark 7/220°C/425°F.
❷ Roll the pastry out on a lightly floured surface into a 5¹/₂–inch (14 cm) circle.
❸ Place the pastry on a floured baking tray, and prick it with a fork.

❹ Spread with the pesto or tomato purée and scatter with the ingredients of one of the toppings.
❺ Bake for 10–15 minutes, or until puffed up and golden.

Filled Baguettes

Chilled baguette dough is available from major supermarkets and is usually found near the butter and chilled pastry. It comes in a cardboard tube and there are usually four baguettes in each tube.

Serves: 1
Preparation and cooking time: 20 minutes
Freezing: not recommended
Selections per serving: see individual fillings
Calories per serving: see individual fillings

tube of mini baguette dough
1 teaspoon skimmed milk, to glaze
For the Pesto, Tomato and Mozzarella Filling
    (215 Calories/2 Carbohydrate; 1/2 Protein;
    10 Optional Calories):
1/2 teaspoon pesto
1/2 oz (15 g) mozzarella cheese, chopped

1/2 tablespoon very finely chopped tomatoes
For the Cheese and Mustard Filling
    (230 Calories/2 Carbohydrate; 1/2 Protein):
1 teaspoon wholegrain mustard
1/2 oz (15 g) Cheddar cheese, grated
For the Ham and Cheese Filling
    (200 Calories/2 Carbohydrate; 1/2 Protein):
1/4 oz (7 g) Cheddar cheese, grated
1/4 oz (7 g) ham, chopped finely

❶ Preheat the oven to Gas Mark 6/200°C/400°F.

❷ Open the tube of dough as directed on the packet and remove one piece of baguette dough by separating it along the perforations. Re-seal the tube and refrigerate it until needed.

❸ Spread the pesto or mustard (if using) on to the dough, leaving a border around the edges. Sprinkle with the desired filling and then roll the baguette up lengthways and pinch the seam firmly to seal.

❹ Score three lines across the top and brush with the milk, to glaze.

❺ Place the baguette on a baking tray and bake for 15 minutes, or until golden. Serve warm.

Weight Watchers note: each baguette is equivalent to 2 Carbohydrate Selections.

Variation: sprinkle the baguette with a pinch of sesame or poppy seeds before baking. This will add 10 Optional Calories.

Crispy Country Mushrooms

The flavour of Stilton really mellows when cooked and makes a wonderful combination with the juicy baked mushrooms.

Serves: 2

Preparation and cooking time: 25 minutes

Freezing: not recommended

Selections per serving: 2 Carbohydrate; 1 Fat;
    2 Protein; 1 Vegetable; 10 Optional Calories

Calories per serving: 390

V

1 oz (30 g) lean rindless back bacon, trimmed

1 teaspoon olive oil

1/4 small onion or 1 shallot, chopped

4 large open-cup mushrooms

1 teaspoon garlic purée

1 beef tomato, skinned, de-seeded and chopped

2 oz (60 g) blue Stilton cheese, crumbled

2 oz (60 g) fresh white breadcrumbs

2 teaspoons chopped fresh parsley

1/2 tablespoon freshly grated parmesan cheese

salt and freshly ground black pepper

To serve:

2 × 1 oz (30 g) slices of crusty bread

2 teaspoons low-fat spread

1 teaspoon chopped fresh parsley

❶ Grill the bacon until crisp, drain on kitchen paper and chop. Preheat the oven to Gas Mark 6/200°C/400°F.

❷ Heat the oil in a small saucepan or frying pan and gently cook the onion or shallot for 2–3 minutes. Remove the stalks from the mushrooms. Chop the stalks and then add them to the onion and cook for 2 minutes more.

❸ Remove the pan from the heat and stir in the garlic purée, tomato, Stilton, breadcrumbs, parsley and bacon. Season to taste.

❹ Divide the mixture between the mushroom caps. Place them in an ovenproof dish or baking tin and sprinkle with the parmesan cheese.

❺ Bake for 15 minutes, or until the topping is golden and the mushrooms are tender.

❻ Meanwhile, toast the bread, spread with the low-fat spread and sprinkle with the chopped parsley. Serve at once, with the mushrooms.

Cook's note: keep an eye out for walnut bread in your supermarket. It really complements the flavour of the mushrooms and Stilton.

V **Vegetarian option:** simply omit the bacon – this will reduce the Protein Selection to 1 per serving.

Tuna and Potato Salad

Try using plum tomatoes in this recipe for their wonderful flavour.

Serves: 2
Preparation and cooking time: 25 minutes
Freezing: not recommended
Selections per serving: 1 Carbohydrate; 1 Fat;
    1 Protein; 2 Vegetable; 40 Optional Calories
Calories per serving: 280

8 oz (240 g) small new potatoes
4 oz (120 g) bag of mixed salad leaves
4 tomatoes, halved and sliced

$1/_2$ **cucumber, chopped**
$1/_2$ **small yellow pepper, cored, de-seeded and**
    sliced in strips
4 oz (120 g) canned tuna in brine, drained
snipped fresh chives, to garnish
For the dressing:
4 teaspoons olive oil
2 teaspoons white wine vinegar
$1/_4$ **teaspoon wholegrain mustard**
salt and freshly ground black pepper

❶ Cook the potatoes in boiling salted water for 15 minutes, or until tender. Drain and refresh under cold running water, and then drain again and cut in quarters.

❷ Arrange the salad leaves, tomatoes, cucumber and pepper in a serving bowl or on 2 plates.

❸ Whisk the dressing ingredients together in a small bowl. Gently toss the potatoes and tuna with the dressing and then pile them on to the centre of the salad. Sprinkle with the snipped chives and serve.

Cook's note: I like to replace 1 teaspoon of the white wine vinegar with 1 teaspoon balsamic vinegar, an Italian vinegar with a distinctive mellow, sweet and sour flavour.

Lamb Kebabs with Minted Yogurt

These spicy kebabs are scrumptious served with the cool, minted yogurt sauce and soft warm pitta bread.

Serves: 2

Preparation and cooking time: 25 minutes

Freezing: not recommended

Selections per serving: 2 Carbohydrate; 1/2 Milk; 2 Protein; 1/2 Vegetable

Calories per serving: 335

V

2 oz (60 g) fresh white breadcrumbs
1 onion, chopped roughly
2 garlic cloves, peeled
1 tablespoon chopped fresh mint
1 tablespoon chopped fresh parsley

4 oz (120 g) lean minced lamb
2 teaspoons ground cumin
2 teaspoons ground coriander
salt and freshly ground black pepper
For the minted yogurt:
1 teaspoon white wine vinegar
5 fl oz (150 ml) low-fat natural yogurt
1 garlic clove, crushed
2–3 teaspoons chopped fresh mint
To serve:
2 × mini pitta breads
green leaf salad
lemon wedges

❶ Put the breadcrumbs, onion and garlic in a food processor and process until evenly and finely chopped. Add the remaining kebab ingredients and process in short bursts until well mixed. Preheat the grill.

❷ Divide the mixture into four, and form each quarter into a sausage shape. Thread the sausages on to four wooden skewers, to make kebabs.

❸ Place the kebabs on the rack of a grill pan and grill for 12–15 minutes, turning frequently, until evenly browned.

❹ Mix the minted yogurt ingredients together.

❺ Warm the pitta breads under the grill, cut them in half and serve with the kebabs, minted yogurt, salad and lemon wedges.

Cook's note: soak the wooden skewers in water for 1 hour before grilling to prevent them from scorching.

Variation: serve with 1 oz (30 g) of ready-made hummus per serving instead of the minted yogurt. This will alter the Selections to 2 Carbohydrate; 1/2 Fat; 2 Protein; 1/2 Vegetable.

V **Vegetarian option:** replace the minced lamb with 6 oz (180 g) canned chick-peas. This will reduce the Protein Selection to 1 per serving.

Crispy Country Mushrooms
Cheesy Potato Rostis
Lamb Kebabs with Minted Yogurt

Cheesy Potato Rostis

These potato rostis are really scrumptious. I like to make them for brunch on a lazy Sunday morning.
They are particularly good with a spoonful of Greek-style yogurt.

Serves: 4 (makes 8)
Preparation and cooking time: 25 minutes
Freezing: not recommended
Selections per serving: 1 Carbohydrate; ¹/₂ Fat;
    1 Protein; ¹/₄ Vegetable; 10 Optional Calories
Calories per serving: 205

Ⓥ if using a free-range egg and vegetarian Cheddar

12 oz (360 g) old potatoes, peeled and grated coarsely
2 spring onions, trimmed and sliced finely
2 shallots, chopped finely
3 oz (90 g) Cheddar cheese, grated
2 tablespoons plain white flour
1 egg, beaten
4 teaspoons creamed horseradish
2 teaspoons sunflower oil
salt and freshly ground black pepper

1 Squeeze any excess moisture out of the grated potatoes and place them in a bowl.
2 Add the remaining ingredients, except for the oil, and stir well.
3 Grease a heavy-based, non-stick frying pan with some of the oil. Place four large spoonfuls of the mixture in the pan and press them down to shape four round flat cakes.
4 Cook the rostis for 3 – 4 minutes until the bottoms are golden, and then turn them over and cook the other sides until golden. Remove with a fish slice and keep warm. Re-oil the pan and repeat with the remaining potato mixture. Serve hot.

Variations: serve with 1 tablespoon of Greek-style yogurt per person and add 20 Optional Calories per serving.

Serve with 1 tablespoon of brown sauce per person and add 15 Optional Calories per serving.

Spicy Mince Tortillas

Wheat flour tortillas are readily available from supermarkets – I love them, as one huge 6-inch (15 cm) tortilla uses only 1 Carbohydrate Selection!

Serves: 2
Preparation and cooking time: 30 minutes
Freezing: recommended
Selections per serving: 1 Carbohydrate; 1 Fat;
    1¹/₂ Protein; 1¹/₂ Vegetable; 55 Optional Calories
Calories per serving: 335

V

2 teaspoons olive oil
¹/₂ small onion, chopped
2 garlic cloves, crushed

¹/₂ **yellow pepper, cored, de-seeded and chopped**
¹/₂ **courgette, trimmed and chopped**
4 oz (120 g) **extra-lean minced beef**
2 teaspoons **mild curry paste**
¹/₂ **teaspoon ground turmeric**
7 oz (210 g) **canned chopped tomatoes**
4 tablespoons **water**
¹/₂ oz (15 g) **raisins**
salt and freshly ground black pepper
To serve:
2 × 6-inch (15 cm) **wheat flour tortillas**
4 tablespoons **low-fat natural yogurt**

❶ Heat the oil and cook the onion, garlic and pepper for 5 minutes. Add the courgette and cook for 4 minutes more.
❷ Meanwhile, brown the mince in a non-stick pan and drain off any excess fat.
❸ Add the mince to the vegetables and stir in the curry paste, turmeric, tomatoes, water and raisins. Bring to the boil and then reduce the heat and simmer gently for 15 minutes. Season to taste.

❹ Meanwhile, wrap the tortillas in foil and place them in a moderate oven until warm.
❺ Divide the mince between the tortillas. Top with a spoonful of yogurt and serve.

V Vegetarian option: use minced Quorn™ instead of beef. Omit step 2 and add the Quorn™ with the ingredients in step 3. This will reduce the Protein Selection to 1 per serving.

Mediterranean Tomato and Bean Soup

This nutritious and filling soup has the fresh Mediterranean taste of tomatoes and garlic. Try to use fresh tomatoes for a really authentic taste.

Serves: 2
Preparation and cooking time: 35 minutes
Freezing: recommended
Selections per serving: 2 Carbohydrate; 1 Fat;
 1 Protein; 3 Vegetable
Calories per serving: 340

Ⓥ

2 teaspoons olive oil
1 large onion, quartered and sliced thinly
4 oz (120 g) potatoes, diced

1–2 garlic cloves, crushed
$^1/_4$ teaspoon cayenne pepper
1 lb (480 g) plum tomatoes, peeled and chopped,
 or 14 oz (420 g) canned chopped tomatoes
$^3/_4$ pint (450 ml) water
6 oz (180 g) canned cannellini beans, rinsed
 and drained
2 tablespoons shredded fresh basil leaves
salt and freshly ground black pepper
2 × 1$^1/_2$ oz (45 g) slices crusty white bread,
 to serve

❶ Heat the oil in a saucepan and sauté the onion gently for 5–8 minutes, until soft. Add the potatoes, garlic and cayenne pepper and cook for 5 minutes more.

❷ Stir in the tomatoes, water and half of the beans. Bring to the boil. Meanwhile, mash the remaining beans to a paste and then stir them into the soup.

❸ Simmer for 20 minutes. Stir in the basil, season to taste and serve with the crusty bread.

Cook's note: this soup makes an ideal starter when entertaining friends. You can leave out the bread and use only $^1/_2$ Carbohydrate, 1 Fat, 1 Protein and 3 Vegetable Selections per serving.

Mediterranean Tomato and Bean Soup
Spicy Mince Tortillas

Main Meals

The meals in this chapter are designed to provide you with the correct amount of Protein and Carbohydrate for balanced nutrition. I have included a wonderful array of dishes to suit any occasion, from a simple supper bake to a stunning pan-fried salmon with fresh avocado salsa – ideal for hassle-free entertaining. You'll discover superb ways to jazz up grilled fish and meat, and if you feel like something lighter, there is a delicious ham salad with a tangy dressing.

Salmon with Avocado and Tomato Salsa

This recipe really makes an impressive meal with which to entertain friends, and as there's no advance preparation, it's perfect for a last-minute supper party. Try it with new potatoes and steamed vegetables.

Serves: 4
Preparation and cooking time: 12 minutes
Freezing: not recommended
Selections per serving: 1 Fat; 2 Protein;
    $^1/_2$ Vegetable; 40 Optional Calories
Calories per serving: 240

4 teaspoons olive oil
4 × 3 oz (90 g) salmon fillets or steaks
freshly ground black pepper

For the salsa:
$^1/_2$ medium-sized avocado, chopped
2 tablespoons freshly squeezed lemon juice
$^1/_2$ red onion, chopped finely
2 beef tomatoes, peeled, de-seeded and chopped
1 tablespoon chopped fresh coriander
salt and freshly ground black pepper
sprigs of fresh coriander, to garnish

❶ Mix together the salsa ingredients and set aside.
❷ Heat the oil in a non-stick frying pan. Season the salmon with pepper and cook for 3–4 minutes on each side.
❸ Serve the salmon with a spoonful of the salsa, garnished with sprigs of coriander.

Variation: if you prefer, you can brush the salmon with the oil and cook it under a preheated grill.

Salmon with Avocado and Tomato Salsa

Pork Chop with Mustard and Guinness

This is one of my husband, Andy's, favourites – perhaps because he gets to drink the remainder of the beer!

Serves: 1
Preparation and cooking time: 18 minutes
Freezing: not recommended
Selections per serving: 3 Protein; 5 Optional
Calories
Calories per serving: 215

3 oz (90 g) pork chop or pork medallion
1 teaspoon English mustard
1 tablespoon Guinness or ale
1 mushroom, sliced thinly
2 tablespoons grated Cheddar cheese

❶ Preheat the grill and cook the pork chop or medallion under a moderate heat for 6–8 minutes on each side.
❷ Meanwhile, mix together the remaining ingredients. Spread them over the meat and grill for one more minute, or until bubbling. Serve immediately.

Cook's note: keep an eye out for pork medallions in your supermarket as they are very tender and usually contain less than 5% fat.

Broccoli, Mushroom and Parmesan Spaghetti

When parmesan cheese is grated finely it goes a long way – you won't believe how much you may sprinkle over this pasta dish!

Serves: 2
Preparation and cooking time: 18 minutes
Freezing: not recommended
Selections per serving: 2 Carbohydrate; 1 Fat;
1 Protein; 3 Vegetable; 40 Optional Calories
Calories per serving: 430

Ⓥ if using vegetarian parmesan

4 oz (120 g) spaghetti
4 teaspoons olive oil

1 onion, chopped
2 garlic cloves, crushed
1 small red chilli pepper, de-seeded and chopped finely
1 red pepper, cored, de-seeded and chopped
6 oz (180 g) broccoli florets
1 courgette, trimmed and diced
5 oz (150 g) mushrooms
4 tablespoons finely grated parmesan cheese
salt and freshly ground black pepper

❶ Cook the spaghetti in a pan of lightly salted boiling water for 12–15 minutes, or until *al dente*. Drain well.
❷ Meanwhile, heat the oil in a frying pan and cook the onion, garlic, chilli and red pepper for 5 minutes, until softened.
❸ Cook the broccoli in boiling water until just tender. Drain well.
❹ Add the courgette and mushrooms to the onion mixture and stir-fry for 4–5 minutes. Season. Stir in the drained pasta and broccoli, along with half of the parmesan cheese. Toss well to combine, and heat through.
❺ Sprinkle with the remaining cheese and serve in warm bowls.

Broccoli, Mushroom and Parmesan Spaghetti
Pork Chop with Mustard and Guinness

Quick Chicken Curry

This Thai-style curry uses prepared Thai red curry paste, which is available in small jars at most supermarkets.
If you haven't tried Thai curry, do have a go – the aromatic light coconut sauce has a wonderful clean, fresh flavour.
I like to serve it on a bed of egg noodles.

Serves: 2
Preparation and cooking time: 20 minutes
Freezing: not recommended
Selections per serving: 3 Carbohydrate; 1 Fat;
    1¹/₂ Protein; 2 Vegetable; 215 Optional Calories
Calories per serving: 550

V

1 teaspoon sunflower oil
4 oz (120 g) skinless, boneless chicken breast,
    cut in strips
1 tablespoon Thai red curry paste
1 teaspoon grated fresh root ginger
1¹/₂ oz (45 g) creamed coconut, dissolved
    in 8 fl oz (240 ml) boiling water

¹/₂ tablespoon light soy sauce
1 teaspoon cornflour, mixed to a paste with
    1 tablespoon water
1 red pepper, cored, de-seeded and sliced finely
6 oz (180 g) baby sweetcorn, halved lengthways
4 oz (120 g) broccoli florets
2 oz (60 g) green beans
5 fresh basil leaves, shredded
2 tablespoons chopped fresh coriander
4 oz (120 g) egg noodles or basmati or Thai rice,
    cooked according to packet directions
To garnish:
chopped fresh coriander
¹/₂ oz (15 g) salted peanuts, chopped

❶ Heat the oil in a deep frying pan or wok, and stir-fry the chicken for 2–3 minutes until cooked through.
❷ Add the curry paste and grated ginger to the pan and stir-fry for 1 minute. Gradually mix in the dissolved coconut, soy sauce and cornflour paste, and bring to the boil.
❸ Stir in the vegetables, reduce the heat and simmer for 5 minutes.

❹ Add the herbs, stir gently and sprinkle with the coriander and peanuts. Serve at once, with noodles or rice.

V Vegetarian option: replace the chicken with 8 oz (240 g) diced firm tofu, added with the vegetables in step 3. This will increase the Protein Selection to 2 per serving.

Quick Chicken Curry

Ham Salad with Mustard and Honey Dressing

Serves: 1

Preparation and cooking time: 20 minutes

Freezing: not recommended

Selections per serving: 2 Carbohydrate; 1 Fat; $^1/_2$ Fruit; 2 Protein; 2 Vegetable; 10 Optional Calories

Calories per serving: 435

---

2 oz (60 g) white or brown rice

$^1/_2$ teaspoon sunflower oil

3 oz (90 g) button mushrooms, sliced

2 oz (60 g) lean ham, chopped

$^1/_2$ red pepper, cored, de-seeded and chopped

$^1/_2$ oz (15 g) raisins

For the dressing:

1 teaspoon low-calorie mayonnaise

1 tablespoon water

2 teaspoons wholegrain mustard

$^1/_2$ teaspoon clear honey

$^1/_2$ teaspoon red wine vinegar

a few drops of Tabasco sauce

salt and freshly ground black pepper

To serve:

watercress

mixed green salad leaves

❶ Cover the rice with plenty of water in a saucepan and bring to the boil. Simmer for 15 minutes, or until tender. Drain and refresh under running cold water and then drain again.

❷ Heat the oil in a small pan and sauté the mushrooms for 2–3 minutes, or until tender.

❸ Mix together the rice, mushrooms, ham, pepper and raisins in a bowl.

❹ Whisk together the dressing ingredients, pour over the rice and toss together.

❺ Arrange some watercress and mixed salad leaves in a serving bowl and pile the rice mixture on top. Serve immediately.

Baked Chicken Kiev
Ham Salad with Mustard and Honey Dressing

Crispy Topped Fish

I developed this recipe for my friend Catherine, who is crazy about crunchy toppings on her food!

Serves: 2
Preparation and cooking time: 22 minutes
Freezing: not recommended
Selections per serving: 1/2 Carbohydrate; 2 1/2
 Protein; 1 1/2 Vegetable; 20 Optional Calories
Calories per serving: 290

2 × 5 oz (150 g) pieces of halibut, cod or haddock fillet, skinned

1 oz (30 g) fresh white breadcrumbs
1 garlic clove, chopped finely
1 oz (30 g) Cheddar cheese, grated finely
1 taco shell, crushed lightly
2 tomatoes, peeled, de-seeded and chopped
1 teaspoon chopped fresh parsley

❶ Preheat the oven to Gas Mark 6/200°C/400°F.
❷ Arrange the fish in a roasting tin.
❸ Mix the remaining ingredients together and spoon them over the fish.

❹ Bake for 15–20 minutes, or until the fish is cooked and the topping crisp and golden.

Baked Chicken Kiev

This low-fat version of the popular Chicken Kiev will appeal to your tastebuds without damaging your waistline!

Serves: 2
Preparation and cooking time: 30 minutes
Freezing: recommended
Selections per serving: 1/2 Carbohydrate;
 2 1/2 Protein; 30 Optional Calories
Calories per serving: 215

2 × 3 oz (90 g) pieces of skinless, boneless chicken breast

1 oz (30 g) low-fat soft cheese with garlic and herbs
1 1/2 oz (45 g) fresh white breadcrumbs
1 tablespoon chopped fresh parsley
1/2 teaspoon garlic purée
1/2 tablespoon plain flour
1/2 beaten egg

❶ Preheat the oven to Gas Mark 6/200°C/400°F.
❷ Make a slit in the side of each chicken piece and fill the pocket with the cheese. Press the edges of the chicken back together and secure the flap with a cocktail stick.
❸ Mix the breadcrumbs with the parsley and garlic purée and spread out on a plate.

❹ Roll the chicken in the flour and then in the beaten egg. Drain well, and then roll in the breadcrumb mixture, pressing the breadcrumbs into the chicken to give it an even coating. Chill until required.
❺ Place the chicken on a baking tray and bake for 20–25 minutes, or until golden. Remove the cocktail sticks and serve immediately.

Aubergine Bake

Instead of a traditional cheese sauce, this recipe uses a combination of fromage frais and grated cheese.
This makes it very quick, deliciously creamy and low in calories – a perfect bake for cooking Weight Watchers style!

Serves: 4
Preparation and cooking time: 40 minutes
Freezing: recommended
Selections per serving: 2 Carbohydrate; ¹/₂ Fat;
2 Protein; 2 Vegetable; 35 Optional Calories
Calories per serving: 445

V

1 tablespoon olive oil
1 aubergine, sliced thickly
1 large onion, chopped
1 red pepper, cored, de-seeded and chopped

1–2 garlic cloves, crushed
6 oz (180 g) extra-lean minced beef
28 oz (840 g) canned chopped tomatoes
2 tablespoons tomato purée
salt and freshly ground black pepper
For the topping:
6 oz (180 g) virtually-fat-free fromage frais
1 egg yolk
2 oz (60 g) Cheddar or parmesan cheese, grated
finely
To serve:
4 × 2 oz (60 g) pieces of crusty bread, warmed

1 Preheat the oven to Gas Mark 6/200°C/400°F.
2 Grease a baking sheet with 1 teaspoon of the oil and lay the aubergine slices on the tray. Bake for 15 minutes, or until golden. Set aside, keeping the oven turned on.
3 Meanwhile, heat the remaining oil in a saucepan and gently cook the onion, pepper and garlic for 5–8 minutes.
4 Brown the mince in a non-stick pan and drain off any excess fat.
5 Add the browned mince, tomatoes and tomato purée to the onion mixture, bring to the boil and then simmer for 10 minutes. Season to taste.

6 Spoon one-third of the mince mixture into an ovenproof dish, and lay half of the baked aubergine slices over the top. Repeat the layers, finishing with the mince mixture.
7 Mix the fromage frais with the egg yolk and season well. Pour evenly over the mince. Sprinkle with the grated cheese and bake for 15 minutes, or until golden and bubbling. Serve immediately with the bread.

V Vegetarian option: simply omit the mince to make a really tasty meat-free version. Remember to reduce the Protein Selection to 1 per serving.

Fish Stew with Garlic Toasts

This is a real favourite of mine. The wine makes this stew very tasty and it goes so well with the garlicky toasts – yes, you can enjoy garlic bread and lose weight!

Serves: 2
Preparation and cooking time: 40 minutes
Freezing: recommended
Selections per serving: 2 Carbohydrate; 1 Fat; 1½ Protein; 4 Vegetable; 85 Optional Calories
Calories per serving: 475

2 teaspoons olive oil
1 onion, chopped
2 garlic cloves, crushed
1 leek, sliced
2 lb (960 g) tomatoes, peeled and chopped roughly

1 tablespoon tomato purée
¼ pint (150 ml) dry white wine
8 oz (240 g) skinned and boned firm white fish (e.g. haddock, cod, hake or halibut), cut in chunks
1 tablespoon chopped fresh parsley + plenty more to garnish
salt and freshly ground black pepper
For the toasts:
2 teaspoons low-fat spread
4 × 1 oz (30 g) slices of baguette
1 garlic clove, chopped finely

❶ Heat the oil in a large frying pan and sauté the onion, garlic and leek for 5–8 minutes.
❷ Stir in the tomatoes, tomato purée, wine and seasoning. Bring to the boil and then reduce the heat and simmer (uncovered) for 20 minutes, until the sauce is thickened. Preheat the grill.
❸ Carefully stir the fish and 1 tablespoon of parsley into the tomato mixture; simmer gently for 5 minutes, or until the fish is just cooked and flakes easily.

❹ Meanwhile, spread the low-fat spread over the baguette slices and sprinkle with the chopped garlic. Place under the hot grill until golden.
❺ Sprinkle the stew with more parsley and serve in warm bowls, accompanied by the garlic toasts.

Variation: stir in 10 small pitted olives with the tomatoes. This will increase the Optional Calories to 120 per serving.

Fish Stew with Garlic Toasts
Crispy Topped Fish

Puddings

Save up a few Selections and you can indulge in a delicious, guilt-free pudding. This chapter will tantalise your taste buds without piling on the pounds. If you have only a matter of minutes, try the scrumptious Fruity Creamy Crunch (page 42), with fresh fruits and crushed biscuits in a creamy yogurt mixture. If you have a little more time, the Lemon and Sultana Filo Triangles (page 44) or spicy Apple and Pear Charlotte (page 46) are absolutely delicious. And for chocolate lovers, I've created a heavenly Chocolate and Raspberry Roulade (page 45). So tuck into some quick and delicious puddings, Weight Watchers style!

Hot Banana Meringues

This recipe uses ready-made meringue nests, which contain only a surprising 60 Calories. The bananas are cooked in margarine and sugar – rich and mouthwatering!

Serves: 2
Preparation and cooking time: 5 minutes
Freezing: not recommended
Selections per serving: 1 Fat; 1 Fruit; 180 Optional Calories
Calories per serving: 275

Ⓥ

2 teaspoons margarine
2 teaspoons soft brown sugar
2 small bananas, sliced lengthways
2 meringue nests
2 × 2 oz (60 g) scoops low-fat vanilla ice cream

❶ Melt the margarine and sugar in a small frying pan. Add the sliced bananas and cook until just softened.

❷ Place a meringue on each serving plate and top with a scoop of ice cream. Spoon the hot bananas over and serve immediately.

Cook's note: for a special occasion, try adding a splash of brandy to the bananas when cooking. Remember to add 50 Optional Calories per serving.

Hot Banana Meringues

Fruity Creamy Crunch

This quick, simple and filling dessert of fresh fruits bound in a thick yogurt mixture with a caramelised topping is absolutely delicious.

Serves: 4
Preparation and cooking time: 12 minutes
Freezing: not recommended
Selections per serving: 1 Fruit; 1 Protein; 120
    Optional Calories
Calories per serving: 210

Ⓥ

1 oz (30 g) all-butter thins biscuits, crushed
    lightly
1 medium-sized peach, halved, stoned and
    sliced thinly

1 small banana, sliced
8 oz (240 g) strawberries, halved
8 oz (240 g) light Greek-style yogurt
4 oz (120 g) ricotta cheese
4 oz (120 g) low-fat fromage frais
1 tablespoon freshly squeezed orange juice
1 tablespoon clear honey
For the topping:
2 tablespoons light muscovado sugar
1 teaspoon ground cinnamon

❶ Preheat the grill and place the crushed biscuits in the base of a flameproof serving dish.

❷ Mix together the fruit and scatter half of it over the biscuits.

❸ Beat together the yogurt, ricotta cheese and fromage frais until smooth. Stir in the orange juice and honey, and then fold in the remaining fruit.

❹ Spread the yogurt mixture over the biscuits and fruit base.

❺ Mix together the sugar and cinnamon and sprinkle over the surface of the pudding. Place under the preheated grill for a few minutes until caramelised. Serve at once.

Variations: You could substitute an equal number of ginger thins for the all-butter thins, for a slightly spicy flavour.

If you can't find ricotta cheese, simply use an extra 4 oz (120 g) of fromage frais.

Lemon and Sultana Filo Triangles
Fruity Creamy Crunch

Lemon and Sultana Filo Triangles

These triangles are like little baked cheesecake parcels – heavenly! As with baked cheesecake, they taste even better the day after they are made, and are wonderful served chilled.

Serves: 8

Preparation and cooking time: 25 minutes

Freezing: not recommended

Selections per serving: 1/2 Fat; 1/2 Protein;
55 Optional Calories

Calories per triangle: 115

Ⓥ if using a free-range egg

7 oz (210 g) low-fat soft cheese

1 tablespoon caster sugar

1/2 beaten egg

grated zest of 1 lemon

2 1/2 oz (75 g) sultanas

**2 oz (60 g) filo pastry, cut in four 7 × 12 inch
(18 × 30 cm) rectangles**

4 teaspoons sunflower margarine, melted

1 tablespoon icing sugar, to dredge

❶ Beat the cheese with the sugar and egg until smooth. Stir in the lemon zest and sultanas. Preheat the oven to Gas Mark 6/200°C/400°F.

❷ Brush the filo pastry sheets with the melted margarine, and cut each sheet in half lengthways (to form two long thin rectangles).

❸ Place a spoonful of the cheese mixture towards the top of each pastry length. Turn the top corner over to the opposite edge to form a triangle and enclose the filling, and continue to fold the pastry until the filling is wrapped securely. Repeat to form eight triangles.

❹ Lightly grease a baking sheet and brush the parcels with the remaining margarine. Bake them for 8–10 minutes, until crisp and golden. Cool slightly and dredge liberally with the icing sugar. Serve cold.

Chocolate and Raspberry Roulade

Save this recipe for a special occasion and invite some chocoholic friends round to share it.

Serves: 4

Preparation and cooking time: 30 minutes
   + cooling

Freezing: not recommended

Selections per serving: $^1/_2$ Fruit; 1 Protein;
   175 Optional Calories

Calories per serving: 255

 V if using free-range eggs

1 Preheat the oven to Gas Mark 4/180°C/350°F.

2 Grease an 8-inch (20 cm) square, shallow cake tin with half of the oil. Line with baking parchment and grease again.

3 Melt the chocolate in a heatproof bowl over a pan of hot water.

4 Whisk the egg yolks and caster sugar together until pale and thick, and then beat in the melted chocolate.

5 Whisk the egg whites until stiff, and fold them into the chocolate mixture, using a metal spoon. Pour the mixture into the prepared tin and spread evenly.

$^1/_2$ **teaspoon sunflower oil**

2 oz (60 g) dark continental chocolate

2 eggs, separated

2 oz (60 g) caster sugar

For the filling:

6 oz (180 g) 8% fat fromage frais

1 tablespoon icing sugar

4 oz (120 g) raspberries

To decorate:

1 teaspoon icing sugar

4 oz (120 g) raspberries

6 Bake for 15 minutes, or until firm and springy to the touch. Turn out immediately on to a fresh piece of baking parchment. Peel off the lining paper and cover the cake with a damp tea towel. Leave for 1 minute, and then roll the sponge up with the fresh paper inside and leave it to cool.

7 Gently unroll the sponge and remove the parchment paper. Spread the cake with the fromage frais. Sprinkle with the icing sugar and scatter the raspberries over.

8 Carefully re-roll the roulade and transfer it on to a serving plate. Decorate with a dredging of icing sugar and scatter around the extra raspberries.

Apple and Pear Charlotte

This spicy apple and pear purée is cooked in a crisp bread casing and is delicious served either straight from the oven or chilled.

Serves: 4
Preparation and cooking time: 40 minutes
Freezing: not recommended
Selections per serving: 2 Carbohydrate; 1 Fat;
   2 Fruit; 70 Optional Calories
Calories per serving: 365

Ⓥ

1 lb (480 g) cooking apples, peeled, cored and
   sliced
12 oz (360 g) pears, peeled, cored and sliced
1 teaspoon ground cinnamon
grated zest and juice of 1 lemon
8 oz (240 g) thin-sliced white bread, crusts
   removed
1¹/₂ oz (45 g) sunflower margarine, melted
2 tablespoons caster sugar
1 oz (30 g) sultanas
1 teaspoon caster sugar, to decorate

❶ Put the apples, pears, cinnamon, lemon zest and juice in a heavy-based pan. Partially cover and cook for 15 minutes, stirring occasionally, until pulpy.

❷ Meanwhile, brush one side of the bread slices with some of the margarine. Grease a 6-inch (15 cm) charlotte mould or cake tin with the remaining margarine and use all but one of the slices to line the base and sides, placing the margarined sides facing the tin, and overlapping the slices.

❸ Stir the sugar and sultanas into the apple and pear purée, and spoon it into the bread-lined tin. Top with the remaining bread slice, tucking the edges in with the other bread slices. Bake for 15–20 minutes, or until the bread is golden and crisp.

❹ Turn the pudding out on to a serving plate and dredge with the remaining caster sugar. Serve warm or chilled.

Chocolate and Raspberry Roulade
Apple and Pear Charlotte

Index